11+ English Semantics

WORKBOOK 3

Homonyms
(Homographs & Homophones)

Dr Stephen C Curran

with Warren Vokes

Edited by
Andrea Richardson and Katrina MacKay

This book belongs to

TUITION

Accelerated Education Publications Ltd.

bluff	press	evening
mole	bar	pitcher
box	case	date
boil	clear	rock

Exercise 1a

1) They waited patiently for the kettle to __boil__ to make a pot of tea.

2) The doctor confirmed that the __mole__ on her back was not malignant.

3) There is a strong group __spirit__ that binds them together.

4) Viewers watching the __live__ broadcast saw the events unfold as they happened.

5) His doctor studied the __case__ notes before making a diagnosis.

6) Before the aircraft was allowed to __fly__, it had to be passed as airworthy.

7) In baseball, the __pitcher__ throws the ball to the batter.

8) "Let's set a __date__ to meet again in August."

9) The team failed to __press__ home the advantage and lost the match.

10) A __wave__ of nostalgia overcame the war veterans.

Score 10/10

Exercise 1b

11) The fire spread relentlessly, consuming the dry, parched __brush__.

12) The mayor agreed to __present__ the prizes at the school speech day.

13) She tried to __bluff__ but her friends saw through her ruse.

14) The humble __bar__ of soap has been replaced with liquid hand wash.

15) Her burnt cakes were __rock__ hard and completely inedible.

16) It was necessary to pack them in a __box__ with layers of protective wrapping.

17) After many years of trial and error they managed to __perfect__ the process.

18) His attempts to rectify the situation only seemed to __compound__ the problem.

19) When the police arrived their first task was to __clear__ the area.

20) He hit another six, thus __evening__ the score.

Score 10/10

live	perfect	
present	compound	
wave	fly	
spirit	brush	

Word Bank
TOTAL
20

cross

. Enclosed group of buildings.
. Cliff with a broad face.
. Transparent.
. Pus-filled abscess on the skin.
. Fight with fists.
. A container.
. Large single-handled jug.
. Currently happening.
. Flawless.
. Make a home.

own

. Massive sea wall.
. Small oval fruit.
. Fishhook with feathers.
. Light contact.
. Except for.
. Alcoholic liquor.
. Device for squeezing something.
. Late part of the day.
. Hand signal.
. Sway to and fro.

Put the mystery letter from the starred square (✳) into box **1** below. Add in the mystery letters from puzzles **2** to **8** then rearrange them to make **Oliver's Mystery Word**. The clue is ATS.

1

Welcome to: The Wonderful World of Homonyms.

Homonyms may be **Homographs** that have the same spelling but a different meaning, or **Homophones** that have the same pronunciation but a different meaning *and* spelling.

Exercises 1 to **11** are **Homographs** and **Exercises 12** to **23** are **Homophones**.

Use the words shown at the top of each page once only in each question and each puzzle.

Score
/ 20

Mystery Word:

Enter your mystery letters here:

1	2	3	4	5	6	7	8

Now rearrange them to make the:

number	count	hold
lap	minute	down
tip	project	fresh
entrance	attribute	change

Across

3. Tilt.
5. Cargo space.
6. Formal dance.
8. To take unfair advantage.
10. To add up.
11. Opening in the eye.
13. Sixty seconds.
15. To bewitch.
18. Flesh around teeth.
19. Wash basin.
20. Youthful.

2

Down

1. Flying mammal.
2. Heavy element.
4. Hurl forward.
7. A characteristic.
9. Direction.
12. Not coarse.
14. Top of thighs.
16. A numeral.
17. Cash.

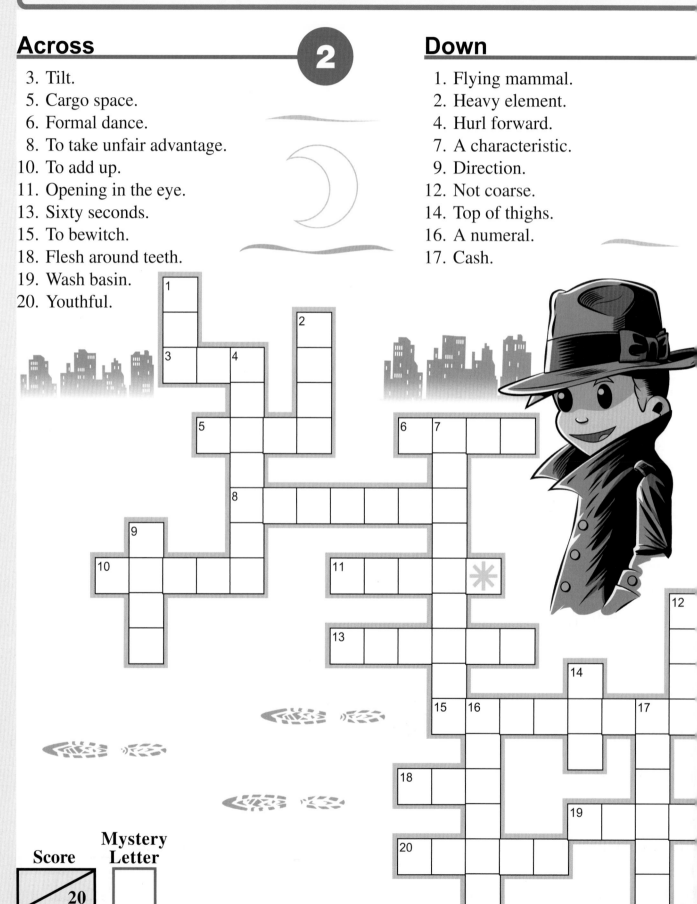

Score

Mystery Letter

20

bat	lead
gum	fine
ball	pupil
exploit	sink

Exercise 2a

1) The _____ to the cave is only accessible at low tide.

2) She spread the tablecloth made of very _____ lace on the table.

3) The mallet is a useful tool to _____ the tent pegs into the dry ground.

4) The sharp _____ of the javelin makes it a very dangerous weapon.

5) As the swelling increased, his leg became _____ still.

6) The thirsty cat took little time to _____ up the milk from the saucer.

7) The _____ of the eider duck is used in pillows and quilts.

8) He picked up his _____ and walked purposefully to the crease.

9) She is a wonderful person and her best _____ is her honesty.

10) He took _____ of the handle and burst through the door. **Score** ⟋ 10

Exercise 2b

11) Sir Francis Chichester's famous _____ took nine months and one day.

12) She is a _____ at Roedean and boards at the school.

13) The greengrocer replaced the tray of oranges with _____ ones.

14) The sight of chewing _____ on the pavements always galled him.

15) _____ Dracula is a ficticious vampire and Transylvanian nobleman.

16) He could not _____ the situation: he just had to endure it.

17) The microscope allows us to see _____ details.

18) The Sherpas took the _____ and the party of climbers followed.

19) Hedgehogs curl into a _____ to protect themselves from preditors.

20) The digital clock could _____ the time onto the ceiling. **Score** ⟋ 10

wind	sewer	band
arms	refuse	subject
duck	ring	converse
match	moped	nail

Across

3

2. To go often to a place.
4. A looped knot.
5. Waste or garbage.
6. Weapons.
8. A strong cloth.
12. Durable circular band.
14. A stick producing fire.
15. To infuriate.
17. A drain for waste.
18. Boy attendant.

Down

1. Abandon an allegiance.
3. A line of things.
4. Instrumental ensemble.
7. Under some authority or control.
9. Polar opposite.
10. Abstain from food.
11. Weighing comparatively little.
13. Moving air.
14. Acted sad or gloomy.
16. Short pointed metal pin.

Score

Mystery Letter

/ 20

Exercise 3a

1) The cooper fitted the last remaining _____ around the barrel.

2) The bride and groom are a perfect _____ .

3) She used an emery board to shape her broken _____ .

4) At sixteen he could apply for a licence to ride a _____ .

5) She is an excellent _____ who stitches everything very neatly.

6) He is a linguist and able to _____ in French, Spanish and German.

7) "Would you _____ the hose back onto the hose reel."

8) If he were to _____ to go with them they may take him by force.

9) It seems that storms and heavy rain are becoming more _____ .

10) It has a small _____ , hence the discounted price.

Score ___/10

Exercise 3b

11) She used the tannoy to _____ the supervisor to go to the check-out.

12) Their house always smelled of the _____ they burned every evening.

13) He was reluctant to discuss the _____ further as she was becoming upset.

14) He dropped his rifle and raised his _____ in surrender.

15) The discussion turned ugly and degenerated into a bitter _____ .

16) He was driven by his love of _____ cars and a quest for speed.

17) "Somebody must be at home: _____ the doorbell again!"

18) A small glimmer of _____ could be seen through the chink in the curtains.

19) He was very tall and had to _____ under the low branches.

20) She secured the _____ line before leaving the boat.

Score ___/10

can	loaf	overlook
sock	accent	firm
compress	does	bass
produce	bank	prune

Across

4

1. Hunted animal or bird.
5. To reverse.
6. To move clumsily or heavily.
9. Dismiss as untrue or trivial.
10. To hit hard.
12. Able to.
13. A dried plum.
14. Compact and solid.
15. A spiny-finned fish.
17. A section of the large intestine.
19. The capacity of a container.
20. To batter something.

Down

2. A loud, disturbing noise.
3. Fresh fruit and vegetables.
4. Female deer.
7. Financial services business.
8. To shrink by applying pressure.
11. Be above something.
16. Main emphasis.
18. Spend time lazily.

Score

Mystery
Letter

20

quarry	back	
lumber	racket	
colon	discount	
buffet	content	

Word Bank
TOTAL
80

Exercise 4a

1) The sailor used a needle and thread from his "housewife" to darn his _____ .

2) He refilled the petrol _____ at the filling station.

3) In America and Canada, felled trees are manufactured into _____ .

4) The nurse applied a _____ to stop the bleeding.

5) The company decided to _____ cars instead of motorcycles.

6) Not _____ with his house, he used his inheritance to purchase a larger one.

7) The police arrested the criminals involved in the illegal _____ .

8) He sings in the _____ section of the choral group.

9) The _____ on the price of the handbag made it an irresistable bargain.

10) " _____ it come with a comprehensive guarantee?"   **Score** [/10]

Exercise 4b

11) "Would you prefer a white or brown _____ ?" asked the baker.

12) All the houses in the locality are built of stone from the nearby _____ .

13) The family _____ of solicitors was founded in 1750.

14) Along the river _____ could be seen the entrances to water rats' burrows.

15) He lived in the south for thirty years but still did not lose his Geordie _____ .

16) She tried not to _____ any evidence but her report was incomplete.

17) It took six visits to the osteopath to realign the vertebrae in his lower _____ .

18) Their holiday included breakfast and dinner from the _____ .

19) He used a _____ in the sentence when it should have been a comma.

20) The arborist knew the best way to _____ the fruit tree.   **Score** [/10]

bear	learned	process
lean	yard	conduct
wound	well	pound
contract	coordinates	intimate

Across

5

4. The bottom or lowest part.
5. Relate spiritually to something.
6. Enthusiastic admirer.
8. Unit of length.
13. Organises something complex.
14. In good health.
16. Drop of fluid from the eye.
17. Bend or incline.
18. Behaviour.

Down

1. Push in forcibly.
2. Enclosure for stray animals.
3. Large furry animal.
5. To shrink or lessen.
7. A collection of abridged articles.
9. Order back.
10. A series of actions.
11. Past tense of 'learn'.
12. Hint quietly.
14. Injury to body.
15. Somebody with persistent disease.

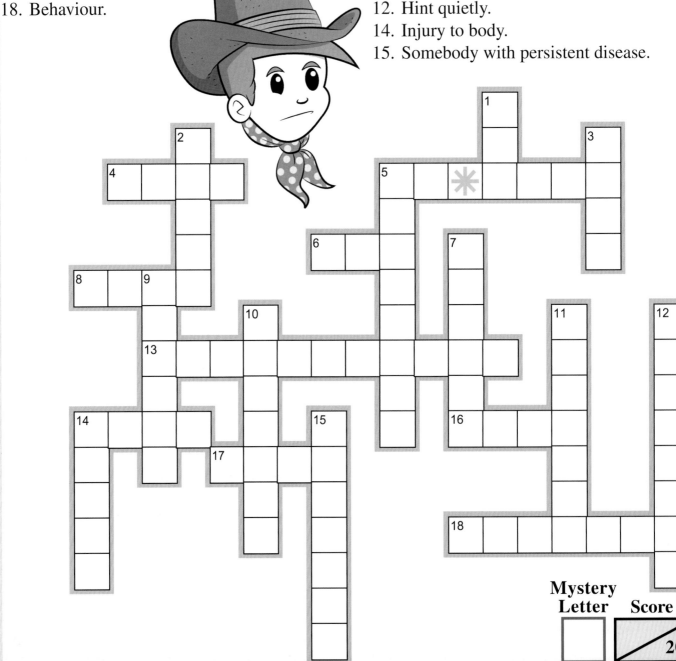

Mystery Letter   Score

2

invalid	**foot**	
fan	**jam**	
tear	**recall**	
digest	**commune**	

Word Bank TOTAL 100

Exercise 5a

1) They had become _____ friends over the years since their schooldays.

2) The crowd saw the choirboys _____ from the Home Office to the Cenotaph.

3) The tower of Pisa has a _____ of 3.99 degrees from vertical.

4) Most kibbutzim in Israel have 200 members within the _____ .

5) He just managed to stop the car a _____ short of the hazard.

6) She _____ the skein of wool into a ball.

7) She could _____ the pain no longer and took two paracetamol tablets.

8) The navigator entered the _____ for their destination and they set off.

9) His mother repaired the small _____ in the knee of his trousers.

Score

10) He continued to _____ the door while ringing the bell.

⧄ 10

Exercise 5b

11) At the rear of the terraced cottage is a small _____ with a washing line.

12) His will has not been witnessed and is therefore _____ .

13) They dropped a stone into the _____ but heard no splash from below.

14) After hours of questioning, her interogators _____ nothing new.

15) Toast and scrambled eggs were easier to _____ after her sickness.

16) They ordered a pot of tea for two with scones, cream and strawberry _____ .

17) They signed the _____ for the house purchase last Wednesday.

18) The old man's _____ was poor: he did not even recognise his brother.

19) The oscillating _____ helped to cool the air in the room.

Score

20) Copper is able to _____ heat and electricity very well.

⧄ 10

console	pen	mind
object	desert	close
swallow	proceeds	putting
compact	polish	incline

Exercise 6a

1) He had a _____ to go for a long walk but the rain put paid to that idea.

2) She bought a new, finer _____ for her watering can.

3) Many _____ airmen flew with the RAF during World War II.

4) After closing the shop, the owner _____ to count the day's takings.

5) It was impossible to _____ her at her mother's funeral.

6) Reversing sensors have made it much easier to _____ a car.

7) The first clap of thunder was followed by a _____ even louder one.

8) She checked she had her make-up _____ and spectacles in her handbag.

9) The _____ of the game Monopoly is to bankrupt the other players.

10) She was alerted by a light _____ on the window pane.

Score ⟋ 10

Exercise 6b

11) The _____ was so steep they had to climb rather than walk up it.

12) "You should chew your food more before you _____ it."

13) The shepherd and his collie dog gathered the sheep into the _____ .

14) He stole the money from her purse when she _____ the room.

15) She told a little white _____ which she thought would not matter.

16) _____ by is a shop that sells almost everything you may need.

17) The native woman carried the load by _____ it on her head.

18) He tried to chop the wood but the three _____ he had were all too blunt!

19) A gust of wind _____ the dustbin, spilling its contents onto the driveway.

20) The camel is often referred to as the ship of the _____ .

Score ⟋ 10

rose	upset	**Word Bank**
lie	tap	**TOTAL**
axes	second	**120**
left	park	

Across

6

. Placing something.
4. Publicly owned area of land.
5. A 60th of one minute.
7. Short and sturdy.
0. Small songbird.
4. Reddish-pink.
5. To be likely to act.
8. To totally abandon a place.
0. Departed.

Down

2. A dramatic change.
3. Money obtained from a transaction.
4. Make smooth or glossy.
5. A water valve.
8. To temporarily watch over.
9. Alliances.
11. A falsehood.
12. To write something.
13. Control panel.
15. Something visible or tangible.
17. To cover an opening.

Score

Mystery Letter

20

sign	hamper	frank
novel	sentence	kid
scale	against	loom
bolt	buckle	harbour

Across

7

3. Lightning flash.
7. Weaving apparatus.
8. Punishment allocation.
9. New and original.
10. In contact by leaning or resting alongside.
13. Meat cooked quickly and lightly.
17. To impede.
18. Public waiting room.
19. Young goat.

Down

1. Sticky substance obtained from tar.
2. Instrument with graduated markings.
3. A bulge, bend or kink.
4. Write one's name.
5. Ship's crew.
6. Computer video display.
11. Gas around a celestial body.
12. Make a deep hole.
14. Safe place of refuge.
15. Bent wire to fasten papers.
16. Open and blunt.

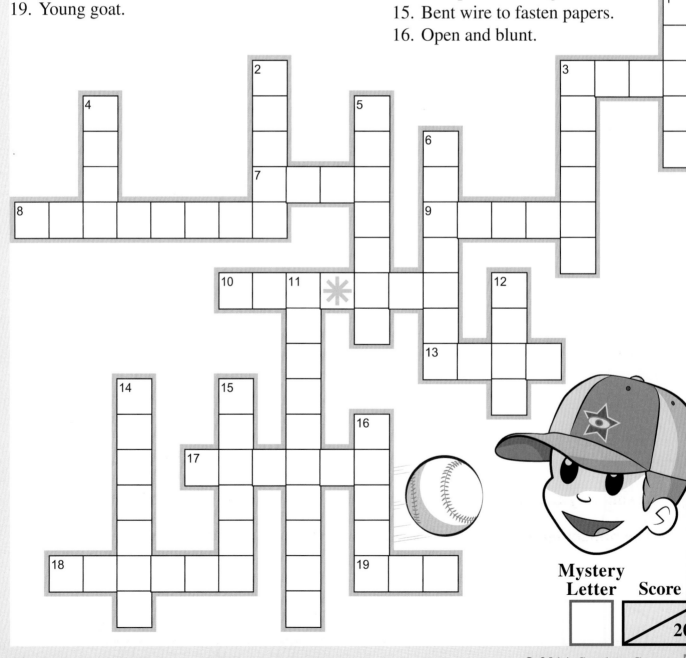

Mystery Letter **Score**

14

atmosphere   **bore**
pitch   **monitor**
staple   **rare**
lounge   **company**

Exercise 7a

1) As soon as she walked into the room she sensed the _____ was tense.

2) Her _____ was a story of two soldiers on the Western Front in World War I.

3) He need not have feared for his safety: he was in good _____ .

4) The nurse checked him every 15 minutes to _____ his condition.

5) The _____ on the envelope confirmed the postage had been prepaid.

6) It is _____ the law to own a firearm without a licence.

7) After her ordeal, she would always _____ a grudge towards her tormentors.

8) "Don't just _____ around the house, go out for some fresh air!"

9) She spread the rug, opened the _____ and laid out their picnic.

10) He tried to _____ her he had won the lottery.   **Score** ⬜ 10

Exercise 7b

11) The warship seemed to _____ menacingly only a mile from the shore.

12) Knowledge of grammar and parsing is required to construct a _____ .

13) The hikers decided to _____ their tent and rest for the night.

14) He is so fit, it is _____ for him to be ill.

15) The foreign ministers took their turn to sit at the table and _____ the treaty.

16) The lesson was a complete _____ and she found it difficult to concentrate.

17) "Don't _____ your food! There is no rush to finish the meal!"

18) Foreigners believed roast beef with Yorkshire pudding was our _____ diet.

19) The mountaineers would have to hurry to _____ the north face before the storm.

20) The _____ broke and he could not fasten his belt.   **Score** ⬜ 10

15

bit	fire	state
soil	pawn	like
dip	hard	spring
mine	hail	fork

Exercise 8a

1) "You can't just _____ a decision like that on me!"

2) She had to _____ her jewellery to raise some cash.

3) Many acting careers have begun with just a _____ part in a film or play.

4) She has been a friend of _____ since we were at school together.

5) Top of the _____ tonight is a famous tenor.

6) He left her a _____ to remind her to meet him at his office.

7) The police report showed there was a _____ of burglaries last month.

8) Whatever the weather, they went for a quick _____ in the sea every morning.

9) She shouted and raised her arm to _____ a taxi.

10) The gunnery officer gave the order to open _____ .

Score

/ 10

Exercise 8b

11) The plumber used a _____ to remove the burrs from the pipe.

12) She used flour, milk and eggs to make the _____ .

13) The farmer tilled the _____ with a harrow before planting the crop.

14) "If you _____ , I'll join you later and we can have a chat then."

15) They poured and levelled the concrete base then left it overnight to go _____ .

16) Their cold and hungry dog was in a dreadful _____ when it was rescued.

17) My _____ reaction was panic; then I realised the ride was quite safe.

18) He finally lost his _____ , shouted at them and stormed out of the meeting.

19) It took them all morning to _____ over the soil on their allotment.

20) "Take _____ of the children while I talk to their parents."

Score

/ 10

initial	batter
charge	note
temper	rash
file	bill

Across

2. To make dirty or stained.
5. Such as.
8. An ordered collection of papers.
9. Lowest value chess piece.
11. A hidden explosive.
12. To hit repeatedly.
15. Pile of burning fuel.
16. Pellets of ice.
17. Difficult or awkward.

Down

1. A bird's beak.
2. Water source.
3. Express in words.
4. To lower, then raise again.
5. To harden metal by heating and cooling.
7. The first letter of a name.
10. To observe something.

Down (continued)

12. Bridle mouthpiece.
13. Thoughtless and impetuous.
14. Attack at a rush.
15. Split into two branches.

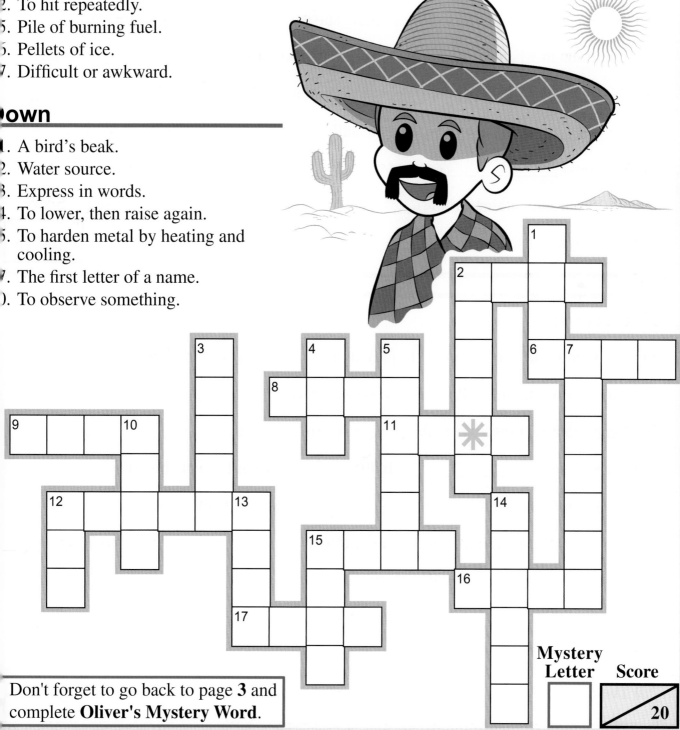

Don't forget to go back to page **3** and complete **Oliver's Mystery Word**.

Mystery Letter **Score**

/20

plain	fuse	grave
ear	periodical	chest
bowl	might	spare
flounder	saw	spruce

Exercise 9a

1) The captain's cabin is located in the _____ of the ship.

2) They stood on the deck to watch a _____ of dolphins race past.

3) She uses herbs, spices and salt to _____ the dish.

4) Strong winds and heavy seas caused the ship to _____ on the rocks.

5) Panic sets in when a mixture of emotions and sensations _____ together.

6) As he is only fifteen, the court deals with him as a _____ .

7) _____ brown envelopes usually contain bills or tax demands.

8) He would _____ down the motorway right on the speed limit.

9) His old head contains a rich _____ of memories of his time at sea. **Score**

10) Lumberjacks use a cross-cut _____ to fell trees.

/ 10

Exercise 9b

11) She graduated from the piano to playing the _____ in church.

12) Guy Fawkes and his fellow conspirators met to _____ the Gunpowder Plot.

13) Deep sea divers discovered the sunken ship in its watery _____ .

14) I carry a set of _____ bulbs in my car when I travel abroad.

15) He ordered his monthly _____ from the local newsagent.

16) A meal in a restaurant before seeing a show makes a _____ night out.

17) A lick of paint and new wallpaper will soon _____ up the room.

18) "I thought we _____ get together and go for a walk at the weekend."

19) A deep _____ and narrow waist give the greyhound its distinctive silhouette.

20) The farmer checked a single _____ of wheat for parasites. **Score**

/ 10

Word Bank TOTAL 180

Across

⑨

2. A lifting door.
5. An evergreen tree of the pine family.
8. To train or instruct somebody in a specific skill.
9. Flat expanse of land.
1. Rigid, strict and uncompromising.
2. Relatively small in quantity, size, or degree.
3. Organ of hearing and balance.
4. Solemn and serious in manner.
5. Mechanical or electrical detonator.
6. A round open dish.
8. Past tense of 'see'.

Down

1. Put away for future use.
3. Traditional division of the year.
4. Great power or influence.
6. Strong rectangular box.
7. An edible flatfish.
9. Recurring or reappearing from time to time.
10. Very great in size, force or degree.
11. To treat somebody leniently.
17. Body part with a specific function.

Put the mystery letters from the starred squares (✳) from puzzles **9** to **15** into their numbered box below, then rearrange them to make **Kate's Mystery Word**.

The clue is a **GREAT WOMAN**.

Enter your mystery letters:

9	10	11	12	13	14	15

Now rearrange them to make the:

Mystery Word:

Score /20

sole	spell	watch
fence	shed	temple
handle	board	ship
strike	suit	mint

Across

10

1. A fluid with substance dissolved it in.
3. To fight with an épée.
8. To deal or cope with.
10. To keep a lookout.
11. To embark.
13. In accordance with the rules.
14. The chorus in a song.
16. A building for worship.
18. To look good on somebody.
19. A short period.

Down

2. Not on time.
4. To train an athlete or other sportsperson.

Down (continued)

5. Only.
6. A small storage structure.
7. A lifting machine.
9. A work stoppage as a protest.
12. To make coins.
15. A symbol representing a number.
17. A section cut from a tree's trunk or branch.
19. To transport over water.

Mystery Letter **Score**

20

solution	figure
coach	crane
fair	log
late	refrain

Exercise 10a

1) The bank's computer will _____ every transaction on your account.

2) Although normally affecting children, the illness may _____ at any age.

3) The _____ to the puzzle is fairly easy to solve.

4) Her loss of earnings did not _____ in the tribunal's conclusions.

5) The floodlights _____ a brilliant light that illuminates the cathedral.

6) Increased house prices could _____ disaster for aspiring homeowners.

7) He took his _____ back to the jewellers to have a new strap fitted.

8) The gold state _____ weighs four tons and is drawn by eight horses.

9) Her charges for _____ and lodgings seem very reasonable.

10) It took all her willpower to _____ from slapping him.   **Score** ⬛ 10

Exercise 10b

11) His _____ grandfather left a substantial legacy.

12) It is customary to serve _____ sauce to accompany roast lamb.

13) With a _____ wind behind them their yacht seemed to skim over the water.

14) He turned his head away but the stone hit his _____ .

15) The crew of the _____ were very attentive to the passengers' needs.

16) The show-jumper's horse knocked down only one _____ , scoring 3 faults.

17) The knight's _____ of armour protected him against swords and arrows.

18) She could not _____ her neck sufficiently to see over the crowd.

19) She turned the _____ of the wringer and fed the clothes through the rollers.

20) There is a large hole in the _____ of his shoe.   **Score** ⬛ 10

trunk	bark	patient
stable	cobble	cabinet
head	kind	right
squash	game	reservation

Exercise 11a

1) On the beach she found a _____ that had fallen from the cliffs above.

2) He telephoned the restaurant to make a _____ for dinner.

3) The magician's trick was to _____ the card unseen by the audience.

4) It took them the whole day to clear the _____ from the attic.

5) "Well, it's a _____ of shelter but it's very poorly constructed."

6) He really enjoys eating _____ , especially venison, rabbit and pheasant.

7) His _____ comments are often offensive although he intends no malice.

8) The receptionist asked the next _____ to go through to see the doctor.

9) The mason used a club hammer and pointer to _____ the stone. **Score**

10) The excited children boarded the _____ to fly to Spain.

10

Exercise 11b

11) In the room is a large _____ displaying all his sporting trophies.

12) The sergeant would _____ out his orders to the soldiers.

13) He _____ home every day at 8.30am and walks to the station.

14) So many people tried to _____ into the lift that the doors would not close.

15) They packed the large _____ ready for the voyage.

16) The equerry ordered the soldiers to _____ their horses.

17) He is the tallest among his _____ group.

18) They failed to _____ in the right direction and were completely lost.

19) "You're not holding the thing by the _____ end!"

20) His son's strength was _____ to his own. **Score**

10

Word Bank
TOTAL
220

Across

11

2. The obverse of a coin.
5. The upper body.
7. To make or repair shoes.
9. A competitive activity with rules.
11. East, when facing north.
12. A tool for smoothing wood.
13. A vegetable of the gourd family.
14. Not sharp.
17. To look very closely or hard.
18. Government leader's advisers.
19. Flat-bottomed Chinese boat.

Down

1. A limiting condition to an agreement.
3. Woman's one-piece garment.
4. Unique.
6. Foliage.
8. Steady and not liable to change.
9. A tropical tree with fronds.
12. Able to endure waiting.
15. To graze the skin.
16. Having a compassionate nature.

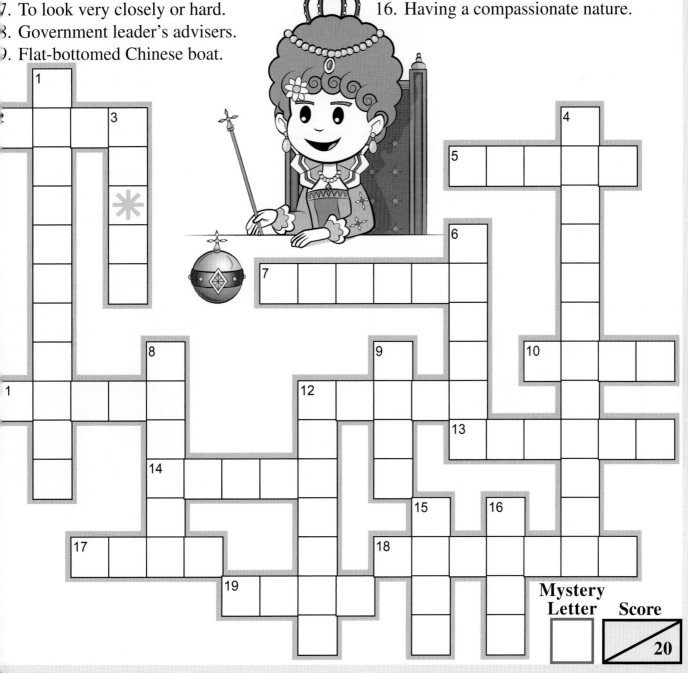

Mystery Letter   **Score**

/ 20

heal	dough	plum
saver	made	wail
might	threw	leach
wet	mail	war

Across

12

4. To enjoy something unhurriedly.
5. A large marine mammal.
7. Past tense of 'wear'.
8. Tiny eight-legged creature.
9. From beginning to end.
13. A German sausage.
15. A narrow flowerbed.
17. Recipient of hospitality.
18. Hit with a sharp blow.

Down

1. True vertical position.
2. Used to express, tiredness, relief, surprise or disgust.
3. Relating to men or boys.

Down (continued)

6. Back part of shoe or sock.
7. To sharpen a tool or weapon.
8. Woman servant.
10. To sit someone elsewhere.
11. To leap or skip playfully.
12. Hinged barrier across a gap.
14. A blood-sucking worm.
16. Mature female deer, rabbit or goat.

Note:

In **Crosswords 12-20**, the answer is a **homophone** of the word in the Wordbank at the top of the page. For example: *'guest'* in the crossword is the **homophone** of *'guessed'* in the Wordbank. You will have underlined the word in the exercises opposite.

17. **G U E S T**

Mystery Letter   **Score**

20

24

© 2014 Stephen Curran

wax	gait
guessed	worst
gamble	receipt
boarder	few

Exercise 12a

> Underline the **incorrect word** and write the correct **homophone**.

1) He did not know the answer but he <u>guest</u> correctly. _guessed_

2) There were very phew loaves left in the baker's shop by lunchtime. _____

3) The outcome of wore is never certain and always unpredictable. _____

4) He was a keen savour and put away at least £20 each month. _____

5) The horse's gate was checked by the vet who found it was slightly lame. _____

6) She felt it was time to increase the rent paid by her border. _____

7) The whale of the police car's siren could be heard approaching. _____

8) It is the wurst tasting sausage I have ever eaten! _____

9) Kneading the doe properly is the secret of breadmaking. _____

10) She asked the cashier for a reseat for her purchase. _____ **Score** ⬜ 10

Exercise 12b

11) She has a plumb job working in the chocolate factory. _____

12) Using only a knife, he maid beautiful carvings from plain driftwood. _____

13) It was whet outside and she needed her umbrella. _____

14) He is known to gambol on the horses but he never seems to win. _____

15) He through the ball for his dog that always retrieved it. _____

16) I'm planning to go out tonight but I mite change my mind. _____

17) Not having a letterbox, he had to collect his male from the sorting office. _____

18) He used a solvent to leech the soluble material from the mixture. _____

19) Long ago, letters were made secure using sealing whacks. _____

20) His wound was deep and took a long time to heel. _____ **Score** ⬜ 10

pore	dual	hangar
vale	maize	presence
adds	faint	rays
peer	medal	moan

Exercise 13a

1) The battered war plane was wheeled into the hanger to be repaired. _____

2) She felt dizzy and sick but desperately tried not to feint. _____

3) After fifteen minutes in the bath, every pour in his body felt open. _____

4) The ship tied up in its birth and the crew lowered the gangplank. _____

5) The squirrel prepared for the winter by burying its horde of nuts. _____

6) Astrologers use a radio telescope to pier into the universe. _____

7) Maze is a cereal crop that originated in South America. _____

8) The speed limit on motorways and duel carriageways is 70 mph. _____

9) Wildlife photographers tract the elephants through the forest. _____

10) They staid in a five star hotel for the weekend. _____ **Score** ⟋ 10

Exercise 13b

11) Her goal is to win a gold meddle at the Olympic Games. _____

12) The rescue team searched over hill and veil for the missing hikers. _____

13) He hid his treacherous intentions under the guys of friendship. _____

14) Exceptionally high tides and heavy seize breached the flood defences. _____

15) "He's never happy: all he does is mown about everything." _____

16) The persistent rain adze to the risk of flooding on low-lying land. _____

17) Building sights sprung up everywhere to meet the demand for housing. _____

18) "Martial the party's supporters and prepare for the general election!" _____

19) Dust particles danced in raze of sunlight streaming into the room. _____

20) Their presents is requested at the board meeting. _____ **Score** ⟋ 10

marshal
sites
tracked
guise

hoard
seas
berth
stayed

Word Bank
TOTAL
300
(including the hidden words)

Across

13

2. To interfere.
3. Sedate and settled in habits or temperament.
5. To completely destroy a place.
6. Gifts.
7. Men (informal).
0. A vertical structural support.
2. Process of being born.
4. Suitable for soldiers or war.
5. An area of land or water.
6. Take hold of something.
7. Formal fight over a matter of honour.

Down

1. A woodworking tool.
2. Cut down.
4. A nail or hook from which something may be hung.
6. Make something flow.
8. Sees something.
9. Face covering worn by women.
11. A deceptive move or action.
13. A large group of people.
14. A confusing network of paths.

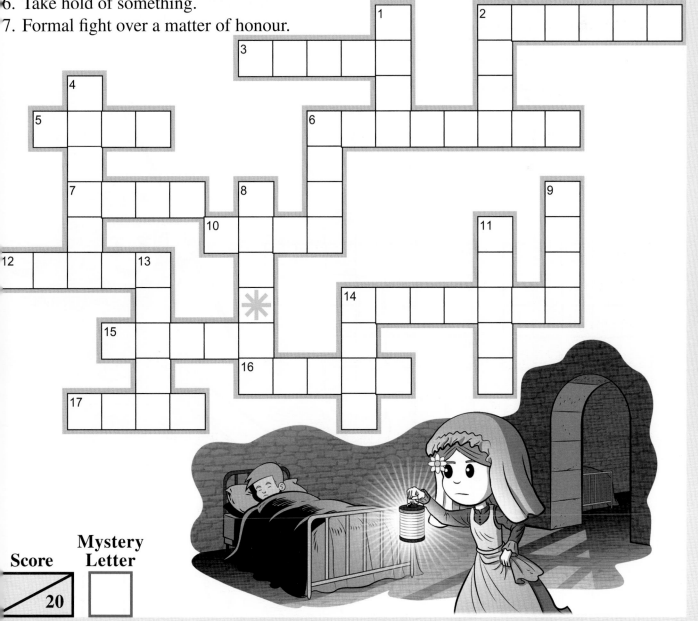

Score / 20

Mystery Letter

27

jam	sighs	incidence
ate	summary	overseas
reek	lead	pail
laps	hole	rows

Across

14

1. Entire.
3. The amount, scope, or degree of something.
5. Prickly shrub with ornamental flowers.
10. Description of warm and dry seasonal weather.
11. One more than 7 and one fewer than 9.
12. Something spiral-shaped.
16. Simple and substantial food.
17. A gap in continuity.
19. Showed the way to others.
20. Forbidden.

Down

2. Supervises.
4. Events.
6. Upright support of a door or window frame.
7. Heaviness.
8. Once a week.
9. Cause something violent and destructive.
13. Fit and strong.
14. Make a structure by joining parts.
15. Lacking in colour or intensity.
18. To remove the outer layer.

Mystery Letter   **Score**

20

band	hail
billed	fair
pear	weakly
wait	whirl

Word Bank TOTAL 340 (including the hidden words)

Exercise 14a

1) They are selling all they have and moving oversees to warmer climes. _____

2) The water at the edge of the lake lapse gently against the shoreline. _____

3) Rose of back-to-back cottages were a feature of Victorian inner cities. _____

4) Fermented pare juice is used to produce an alcoholic perry. _____

5) She asked the hotel doorman to hale a taxi for her. _____

6) So much information was imparted that it made her head whorl. _____

7) He has fare skin, so he takes care to use plenty of sun screen. _____

8) Digging the whole took much longer than the time spent refilling it. _____

9) The roadworks caused a half mile traffic jamb. _____

10) She half-filled the pale with milk from the cow. _____

Score

/ 10

Exercise 14b

11) During their journey they eight the sandwiches their mother had made. _____

12) She told her daughters to weight on the corner and not to cross the road. _____

13) He build his customers every month for the work he had carried out. _____

14) The workmen replaced the led piping with copper. _____

15) Size of relief could be heard when the opposition failed to score. _____

16) The weather forecast followed the news summery. _____

17) The incidents of part-time working varies across the country. _____

18) The kitchen fire caused the whole house to wreak of smoke. _____

19) He replied to the advert for a drummer to join the banned. _____

Score

/ 10

20) "I'm fine," she said as she nodded weekly. _____

knead	chews	stile
some	caster	links
ail	bean	succour
hall	cheap	wood

Exercise 15a

1) The verdict brought no sucker to the victims of his crimes. _____

2) In every race there is only won winner. _____

3) The tents and food aid brought sum relief to the refugees. _____

4) Bread making requires the baker to need the dough well. _____

5) "Wipe your feet on the doormat in the haul before walking in." _____

6) The child left the green been on her plate and refused to eat it. _____

7) Modern drugs cure or relieve many diseases that ale human beings. _____

8) A ruminant is a hoofed animal that choose the cud. _____

9) "Play for me again the cord of Eb minor." _____

10) The navel display at Portsmouth is not to be missed. _____

Score [/10]

Exercise 15b

11) The dry would caught and burned fiercely. _____

12) In the 19th century the poet, Keats, wrote 'Owed on a Grecian Urn'. _____

13) It looked too cheep to sell for such an enormous sum. _____

14) The Panama Canal lynx the Pacific and Atlantic Oceans. _____

15) They climbed over the style to continue along the footpath. _____

16) A castor on the chair is broken and needs to be replaced. _____

17) Two diamond shaped pips below a crown denote the rank of kernel. _____

18) The ball-boy throes the ball to the tennis player for her to serve. _____

19) He has severe burns that require a skin graphed. _____

20) The drummer hit the symbol on the off-beat. _____

Score [/10]

cymbal   **throws**
naval   **graft**
chord   **one**
colonel   **ode**

Word Bank
TOTAL
380
(including the hidden words)

Across

1. Brown oily aromatic substance.
4. The central part.
5. A shoot growing from a root.
9. String or rope.
0. Pull or drag something.
4. Decide from a range of different options.
5. Total amount.
6. Require.
7. Used in making a polite request.

Down

1. Sound made by a young bird.
2. Was financially in debt to somebody.
3. Alcoholic drink.
5. Hollow on the surface of the stomach.
6. Way of writing or performing.

Down (continued)

7. Data was added to a chart.
8. Effects of severe physical pain.
11. Past participle of 'be'.
12. Achieved victory.
13. Something that represents something else.
18. A short-tailed wild cat with tufted ears.

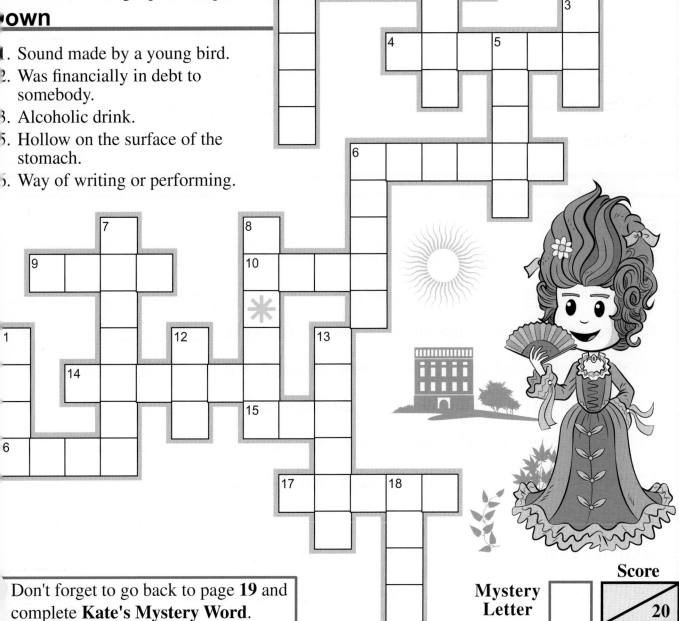

Don't forget to go back to page **19** and complete **Kate's Mystery Word**.

Mystery Letter

Score

/ 20

trussed	choir	miners
sail	pride	blew
cygnet	soared	brewed
sleight	pole	roll

Exercise 16a

1) Emerging from the pit, the minors' faces were black with coal dust. _____

2) She raised the spoon to her lips and blue on it to cool the soup. _____

3) Good news on the economy and the stock market sword. _____

4) They built a four story house on the site of the bungalow. _____

5) He asked the referee to brush the bays on the snooker table. _____

6) They all held their breath: it was a tents moment. _____

7) The heat from the blaze was so intents that no-one could approach. _____

8) Lewis Clarke became the youngest person to ski-trek to the South Poll. _____

9) The crocodile's jaws were securely trust with a large elastic band. _____

10) To repair the windmill's sale was a difficult task. _____ **Score** ⟋ 10

Exercise 16b

11) The pair of swans are very protective of their only signet. _____

12) After his skis flew off he began to role down the slope at high speed. _____

13) Porridge with honey is the only breakfast serial he will eat. _____

14) The crew prepared to gibe the clipper away from the wind. _____

15) Details of braking news scrolls across the bottom of the screen. _____

16) Fields of lavender in the south of France are a cite for sore eyes. _____

17) With a deft slight of hand the magician palmed the card. _____

18) The scandal brood for several weeks before the story broke. _____

19) It was her indefatigable sense of pried that spurred her on. _____

20) Every Sunday he sings in the church quire. _____ **Score** ⟋ 10

Across

16

1. A survey of the public.
2. The colour of a cloudless sky.
3. A mocking remark.
5. Factual or fictional narrative.
6. Very small in size, degree, amount, or importance.
9. Slowing or stopping a machine or vehicle.
11. An animal's or bird's young.
12. Confidence and reliance.
16. A story published or broadcast in parts.
17. One twentieth of a ream of paper.
18. A small seal.

Down

1. Opened using leverage.
2. Areas or compartments used for a particular purpose.
4. Plans or purposes.
7. Hand-held, long-bladed weapon.
8. Not legally adults.
10. Opportunity to buy goods at a discount.
13. An acting part.
14. Collapsible, movable, fabric shelters.
15. To name somebody in a court case.

Put the mystery letters (✳) from puzzles **16** to **23** into their numbered box below then rearrange them to make **Dickens's Mystery Word**.
The clue is **OPTICIANS**.

Enter your mystery letters here:

16	17	18	19	20	21	22	23

Now rearrange them to make the:

Mystery Word:

Score ⬜/20

wield   canvas   suede
hair   knows   suite
road   peal   told
whirred   vain   forth

Across   17

2. One of four parts.
6. Rung slowly and repeatedly.
7. Turned quickly.
10. Unit of language.
11. A mutual agreement.
12. Increase strongly and suddenly.
14. Change.
16. Swung back and forth.
17. Propelled a boat using oars.
19. Channel joining two seas.

Down

1. Organ of smell.
3. Large member of rabbit family.
4. Fruit or vegetable skin.
5. Turn a handle in a circular motion.
8. Eagle's nest.
9. Houses and land owned by medieval noblemen.
12. Tasting or smelling of sugar.
13. A rotating blade.
15. Asking people for their opinions.
18. An award for the winner.

E
N H
N F D
Z X T P
F T D Z U
H T P N F D
Z D T N U H P
H P X T Z F N
P D T N U H Z

Mystery Letter   **Score**

2

© 2014 Stephen Curran

pries	whined
manners	airy
packed	straight
altar	serge

Exercise 17a

1) The lights came on when the electric generator word into life. _____

2) They were delighted with the enormous hotel sweet. _____

3) Monarchs often wheeled great power over their subjects. _____

4) The colour of the hare on his head differed from that of his beard. _____

5) The bride and groom emerged from the church to a peel of bells. _____

6) "Guards! Bring fourth the prisoner so I may question him further." _____

7) The addition of skylights made their loft bright and eyrie. _____

8) Bread and wine of holy Communion stood on the alter. _____

9) "I'm not to blame; I was tolled to dispose of the documents!" _____

10) A coat made of surge should last a lifetime. _____   Score ⬛ 10

Exercise 17b

11) The car boot is pact with everything we need for the holiday. _____

12) The canvass tent was replaced as it was no longer waterproof. _____

13) They searched everywhere for a replacement but it was all in vane. _____

14) It's no longer a secret, everyone nose how the film ends. _____

15) Her parents do not seem concerned about her appalling manors. _____

16) The railway tracks stretched in a strait line way into the distance. _____

17) The strong wind wind and moaned through the trees. _____

18) Following the rowed seemed the best way to find their way in the fog. _____

19) He uses a wire brush to buff his swayed shoes. _____   Score

20) "She's a busybody and prize into everyone's affairs." _____   ⬛ 10

waive	coward	lessen
preys	stake	use
relaid	flea	core
boy	hoes	bough

Exercise 18a

1) It was a serious crash but nun of the passengers was seriously injured. _____

2) News of the disaster did not phase her at all. _____

3) He has an enormous appetite for such a small buoy. _____

4) The boat's painter is securely tied to a steak driven into the ground. _____

5) He was branded a cowered after he ran from the battlefield. _____

6) The committee decided to wave the restrictions imposed last year. _____

7) "I can't ewes this pen; it's run out of ink." _____

8) After shouting so much supporting his team, he became quite horse. _____

9) The Earth's corps is molten in parts. _____

10) He is known as the Texan oil barren. _____

Score
/ 10

Exercise 18b

11) Taking his queue from the chairman, he began his presentation. _____

12) She hates to see weeds in her borders so she hose them regularly. _____

13) He took the dog into the garden and administered the flee powder. _____

14) Their tour guide picked a bury and assured them it was edible. _____

15) He used a chamois leather to wipe the due from the car's windows. _____

16) The carpet had stretched badly and had to be relayed. _____

17) Removing many non-essential items, we managed to lesson the load. _____

18) The weight of the fruit was bending every bow on the tree. _____

19) The bully praise on boys that are weaker than him. _____

20) He always enjoys a current bun with his cup of tea. _____ Score
/ 10

baron	berry
faze	currant
hoarse	dew
cue	none

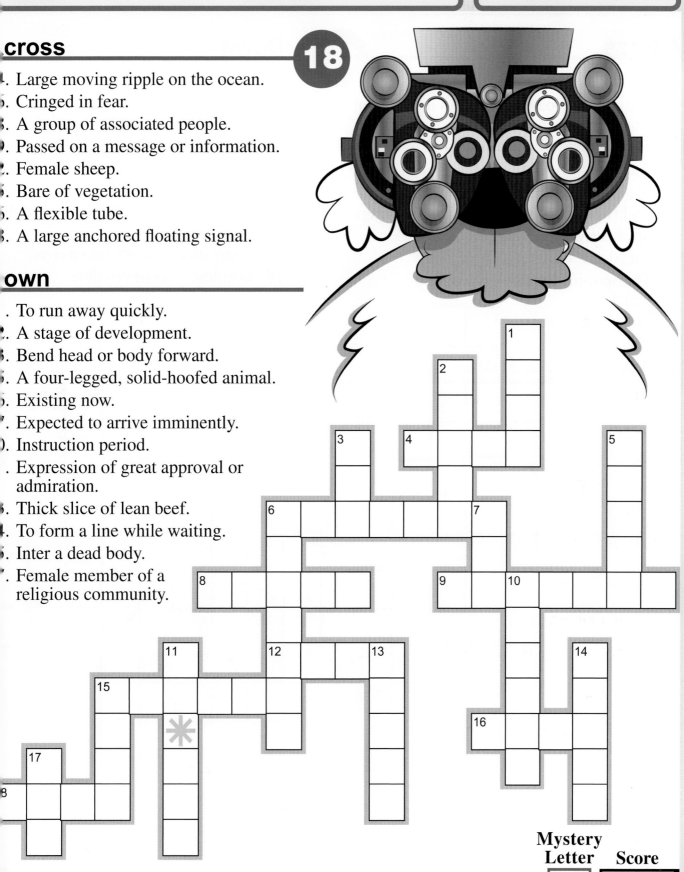

cross

1. Large moving ripple on the ocean.
5. Cringed in fear.
6. A group of associated people.
9. Passed on a message or information.
2. Female sheep.
5. Bare of vegetation.
5. A flexible tube.
8. A large anchored floating signal.

own

. To run away quickly.
2. A stage of development.
3. Bend head or body forward.
5. A four-legged, solid-hoofed animal.
6. Existing now.
7. Expected to arrive imminently.
0. Instruction period.
. Expression of great approval or admiration.
3. Thick slice of lean beef.
4. To form a line while waiting.
5. Inter a dead body.
7. Female member of a religious community.

Mystery Letter

Score / 20

creak	perse	aisle
incite	died	rye
racket	brews	sole
rued	callous	yoke

Across

1. Ill-mannered.
3. Platform for loads that allows mechanical handling.
5. To give pleasure or satisfaction.
7. Agree to something.
10. Skin discolouration caused by injury.
12. Lightweight bat with a network of strings.
14. Spirit surviving death.
15. An island.
16. Transporting by animals working together.
17. The yellow of an egg.
19. A patch of thickened skin.

19

Down

2. Coloured by soaking in a colouring solution.
3. Draw lips together at the sides.
4. Damages by use or rubbing.
6. Legal inheritor.
8. Amusing and ironic.
9. To plant land with seeds once more.
11. Perceptiveness.
13. A stream that flows into a river.
18. Smallest amount possible.

Mystery Letter   Score

teeming	**leased**	**Word Bank**
pleas	**wares**	**TOTAL**
recede	**ascent**	**540**
air	**palate**	*(including the hidden words)*

Exercise 19a

1) The coroner opened the inquest for the men who had dyed. _____

2) Her promotion gave her soul responsibilty for the whole team. _____

3) She spun round when she heard the floorboard creek. _____

4) "Be sure to leave a wide isle between the rows of seats." _____

5) Their scheme had failed and he rude the day he became involved. _____

6) He plied his trade and sold his wears at local car boot sales. _____

7) So much exposure to brutality left him callus and dangerous. _____

8) A wine taster requires a very discerning pallet and nose. _____

9) They began their assent of the mountain at dawn. _____

10) "It's teaming outside; fetch a brolly!" _____   Score 10

Exercise 19b

11) The next day the bruise on her face had turned a shade of purse. _____

12) She bruise a lovely cup of tea. _____

13) It seemed to have vanished into thin heir and could not be found. _____

14) The property was least immediately after it was advertised. _____

15) They stood on deck and watched the land reseed in the distance. _____

16) His intention is to insight the workers to take strike action. _____

17) Every morning he would yolk the two draft animals together. _____

18) "Stop making such a racquet; I can hardly hear myself think!" _____

19) His favourite drink was a very small glass of wry whiskey. _____

20) She was unmoved by their please for leniancy. _____   Score 10

chute	stationary	paced
moose	mantel	side
wine	mustard	retch
patience	sty	coarse

Exercise 20a

1) She stroked the pig and discovered its hair is very course. _____

2) He asked the waitress for mustered to have with the roast beef. _____

3) He asked the other fishermen what bate they were using. _____

4) The old clock had stood on the stone mantle for many years. _____

5) The oil spill, being non-missable, floated on the surface of the sea. _____

6) The cyclist failed to stop and ran into the back of the stationery bus. _____

7) Peering over the cliff edge, he saw it was a shear drop to the beach. _____

8) "Would you prefer red or white whine with your meal?" _____

9) The swimming pool has a water shoot and diving boards. _____

Score

10) Mucking out the pig stye is an unenviable job. _____

/ 10

Exercise 20b

11) A short in the circuit caused the current to ark across with a flash. _____

12) The heart is the hardest working mussel in your body. _____

13) The football field is on the far sighed of the park. _____

14) He walked from the start and paste out the distance to the finish. _____

15) "You must learn to have patients and not act so hastily." _____

16) She recommended to her friend the instructor who taut her to drive. _____

17) It was necessary to sensor the letters sent home by service personnel. _____

18) They were offered a lone to buy the car but they did not need it. _____

19) The overpowering smell of rotting flesh made him wretch. _____

20) Antelope, caribou and mousse are all types of deer. _____ **Score** / 10

40

loan

taught

sheer

miscible

muscle

bait

censor

arc

Word Bank

TOTAL

580

(including the hidden words)

Across

20

2. Direction travelled.
7. Wire mesh in a gas lamp.
). Fire a weapon.
2. Swelling on an eyelid.
4. To cut off.
5. Made an exhaling sound.
5. Stretched tightly.
7. Edible marine mollusc.
). Noah's ship.
). Could be avoided.

Down

1. To hold something back.
3. Things used for writing.
4. Light, sweetened dessert.
5. An adhesive mixture.
6. A detecting instrument.
8. People given medical treatment.
9. A person in trouble or distress who evokes pity.
11. Gathered people or things together.
13. Grumble peevishly.
18. Solitary.

Mystery Letter

Score

/20

peeked   leak   root
unreal   earn   place
days   rough   eyelet
groan   peace   lea

Across

2. Large, flat, edible seafish.
4. Very large and impressive.
6. Unwind.
7. A fancy pleated collar.
8. Caused somebody to be in a bad mood or feel resentful.
10. Edible plant.
12. Part detached from a larger whole.
15. Disgusting.
16. Perceived with the eyes.
17. A channel through which something flows.
19. Making something watertight or airtight.

Down

1. To pay for the use of something.
3. Audibly.
5. A way, path or road for travelling from one place to another.
9. A confused state.
10. Shelter from the wind.
11. Having developed and matured.
13. A small island.
14. Shallow depressions in a surface.
18. Vase for somebody's ashes.

Mystery Letter   Score

© 2014 Stephen Curran

scene	vial
ceiling	grate
allowed	higher
ducked	dense

Word Bank
TOTAL
620
(including the hidden words)

Exercise 21a

1) The firemen were blinded by the dents smoke throughout the building. _____

2) Hanging from the high sealing are three huge chandeliers. _____

3) You could hear the ship's timbers grown and creak in the swell. _____

4) She remembers the daze before computers and mobile phones. _____

5) To reach the guttering he had to climb hire up the ladder. _____

6) "Don't make a seen, but I think they've scratched your car." _____

7) The Piece Treaty of Versailles was signed on 28 June 1919. _____

8) "Be advised that no-one is aloud to talk during the examination." _____

9) At the interview, the candidate duct all the questions about her past. _____

10) He took out a small vile and drank the contents. _____   Score ⬜ / 10

Exercise 21b

11) He relied upon overtime to enable him to urn enough to live on. _____

12) She opened the bedroom door and piqued in to check the children. _____

13) The increase in income tax is the main route of their discontent. _____

14) Gale force winds made for a very ruff sea crossing to Ireland. _____

15) 'The lowing herd wind slowly o'er the lee'; from a poem by Thomas Gray. _____

16) His constant criticising began to great on her. "Stop it!" she cried. _____

17) The tapestry has a metal islet in each corner for easy hanging. _____

18) "I was reading and lost my plaice when you interrupted me." _____

19) The scene was unreel; the whole building was in flames. _____   Score

20) The company needs to plug the leek in its finances. _____   ⬜ / 10

brake	cellar	passed
crews	profit	oar
bald	gilt	waist
pedal	frees	time

Exercise 22a

1) Down in the seller, the rats can be heard scrabbling around for food. _____

2) He was unable to row with only one ore, so he paddled the boat instead. _____

3) A jumbo guitar has a wider waste than a classical guitar. _____

4) There is no thyme like the present to get things done. _____

5) A very light knocking could just be herd above the engine noise. _____

6) His defence lawyer asked for bale but the judge refused the request. _____

7) "It's not a frog, it's a towed with dry warty skin." _____

8) The job was not suitable for a school lever without work experience. _____

9) On Sundays she would peddle five miles to her aunt's house. _____

10) The gates, coated in guilt, looked magnificent. _____   **Score** [/10]

Exercise 22b

11) "Use the break to slow the car before turning the corner." _____

12) In its third year of trading the company began to make a prophet. _____

13) After so many wet weeks they craved for an end to the reign. _____

14) She searched through countless magazines for her ideal bridle gown. _____

15) A squirt of penetrating oil often frieze a rusted nut and bolt. _____

16) Although he had a beard, by the age of forty he was completely bawled. _____

17) The Oxford and Cambridge cruise prepared for the start of the race. _____

18) She crossed the road and past by on the opposite pavement. _____

19) She worked like a Trojan and never seemed to tyre. _____   **Score**

20) With a smaller engine the van lax acceleration. _____ [/10]

tire   leaver
heard   rain
bail   lacks
bridal   toad

Word Bank
TOTAL
660
(including the hidden words)

cross

22

2. Somebody predicting the future.
4. Culinary herb.
5. A large group of animals.
8. Circular rubber edging for a wheel.
0. Use carelessly and extravagantly.
2. A large bundle or package.
3. Legal culpability.
5. Harness for a horse's head.
6. Decorative band along a wall.

own

. A person offering something for sale.
2. To sell goods.
3. Mineral from which metal is extracted.
5. Beyond something.
7. A rigid bar used to move or lift a load.
8. Pulled along by rope or chain.
9. A pleasure trip by sea.
. To rule a nation as its king or queen.
2. Separate into pieces.
4. Not strict or careful enough.
5. Shouted in a loud, aggressive voice.

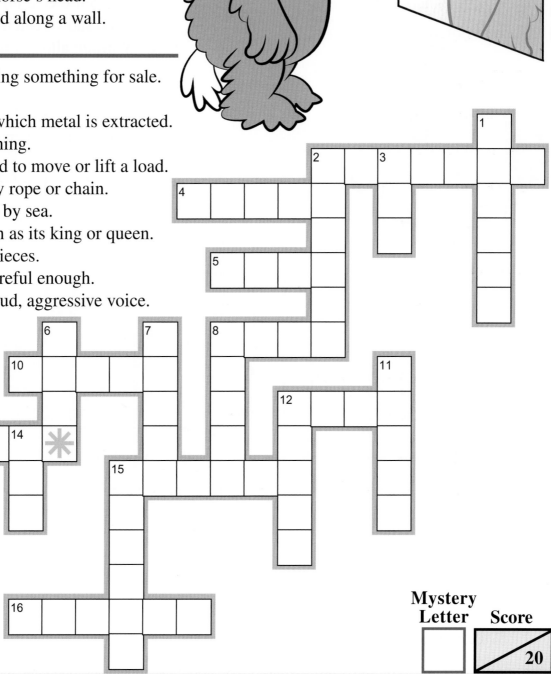

Mystery
Letter   Score

20

serf	rues	slay
flair	fir	frays
steal	find	complement
scull	humerus	tear

Across

23

3. Funny, witty or amusing.
5. A grammatical string of words within a clause or sentence.
7. Foamy waves breaking on the seashore.
9. A clever trick to deceive others.
11. A sudden blaze of light.
14. A stand for a coffin.
15. Courage, spirit, or strength of character.
17. A current of cold air.
19. Painful or tender.

Down

1. To express sadness at somebody's death.
2. A statement to express praise and approval.
4. A waterside platform where boats are loaded and unloaded.
5. A piece of glass in a window.
6. Skeletal part of the head.
8. Soft dense coat on a hairy mammal.
10. Open snow vehicle pulled by horses
12. A strong alloy of iron and carbon.
13. Punished by imposing a payment.
16. A colour.
18. A row of seats placed one above and behind each other.

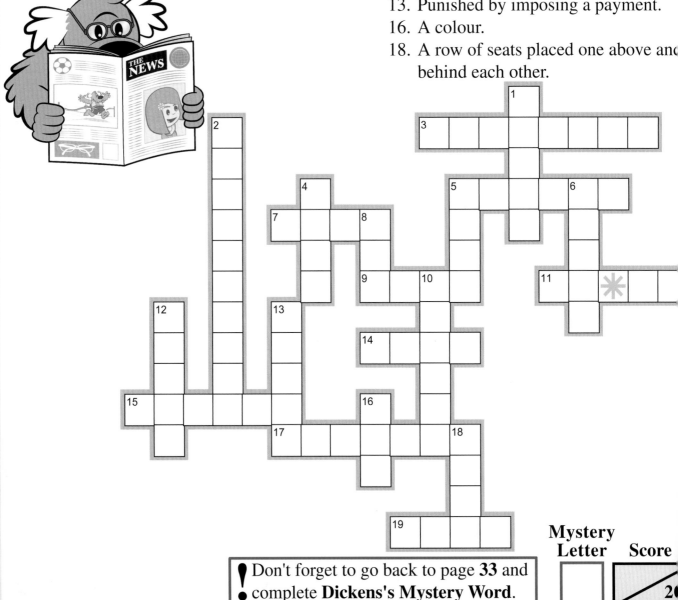

Don't forget to go back to page **33** and complete **Dickens's Mystery Word**.

Mystery Letter   Score

© 2014 Stephen Curran

beer	key
draft	morn
soar	pain
hew	metal

Exercise 23a

1) She wiped the tier from her eye and suppresssd a sob. _____

2) "I've looked everywhere but can't fined my book anywhere." _____

3) You need to wear gloves to pick up the sharp mettle swarf. _____

4) I know he ruse the day he failed to take the job he was offered. _____

5) At early mourn I went away with cheerful heart to work the day. _____

6) Her tutor says she has a real flare for drawing and painting. _____

7) Constant danger causes stress and phrase the nerves. _____

8) He fell awkwardly and broke his humorous. _____

9) A surf was little better off than an enslaved labourer. _____

10) Knowledge and endeavour are the quay to success. _____ Score [/ 10]

Exercise 23b

11) "Would you like a bier, or do you prefer a soft drink?" _____

12) He is evidently in a lot of pane and needs medical assistance. _____

13) The cones littered the ground at the foot of the fur tree. _____

14) The sword St. George used to sleigh the dragon was named *Ascalon*. _____

15) He placed his skull on the river and carefully climbed into it. _____

16) The waiter recommended an exquisite wine to compliment the meal. _____

17) It was only the first draught of the report and could be improved. _____

18) The policeman saw him steel the bicycle from outside the library. _____

19) They used a machete to hue a way through the jungle. _____ Score

20) Inflation caused prices to sore to unprecedented levels. _____ [/ 10]

Homographs Word List

accent	compress	handle	number
against	conduct	harbour	object
arms	console	hard	organ
atmosphere	content	hatch	overlook
attribute	contract	head	page
axes	converse	hold	palm
back	coordinates	incense	park
ball	count	incline	patient
band	crane	incomparable	pawn
bank	date	initial	peer
bar	defect	intimate	pen
bark	desert	invalid	perfect
bass	digest	jam	periodical
bat	dip	junk	pitch
batter	discount	kid	pitcher
bear	does	kind	plain
bill	down	lap	plane
bit	dress	late	polish
bluff	duck	lead	pound
blunt	ear	lean	present
board	entrance	learned	press
boil	evening	leaves	proceeds
bolt	exploit	left	process
bore	fair	lie	produce
bow	fan	light	project
bowl	fast	like	prune
box	fence	live	pupil
brush	figure	loaf	putting
buckle	file	log	quarry
buffet	fine	loom	racket
cabinet	fire	lounge	rare
can	firm	lumber	rash
case	flounder	match	recall
change	fly	might	refrain
charge	foot	mind	refuse
chest	fork	mine	reservation
clear	frank	minor	right
close	frequent	mint	ring
coach	fresh	minute	rock
cobble	fuse	mole	rose
colon	game	monitor	row
commune	grave	moped	saw
compact	gum	nail	scale
company	hail	note	school
compound	hamper	novel	season

48

Homographs Word List

cond
ntence
wer
ed
ip
gn
1k
ck
il
le

solution
spare
spell
spirit
spring
spruce
squash
stable
staple
state

stern
store
strike
subject
suit
swallow
tap
tear
temper
temple

terrific
tip
trunk
upset
watch
wave
well
wind
wound
yard

Homophones Word List

ds / adze
1 / ale
r / heir
ry / eyrie
sle / isle
lowed / aloud
tar / alter
c / ark
cent / assent
e / eight
il / bale
it / bate
ize / bays
ld / bawled
nd / banned
ron / barren
an / been
er / bier
rry / bury
rth / birth
lled / build
ew / blue
arder / border
ugh / bow
y / buoy
ake / break
eaking / braking
ewed / brood
ews / bruise
dal / bridle
lous / callus

canvas / canvass
caster / castor
ceiling / sealing
cellar / seller
censor / sensor
cereal / serial
cheap / cheep
chews / choose
choir / quire
chord / cord
chute / shoot
coarse / course
colonel / kernel
complement / compliment
core / corps
coward / cowered
creak / creek
crews / cruise
cue / queue
currant / current
cygnet / signet
cymbal / symbol
days / daze
dense / dents
dew / due
died / dyed
dough / doe
draft / draught
dual / duel
ducked / duct
earn / urn

eyelet / islet
faint / feint
fair / fare
faze / phase
few / phew
find / fined
fir / fur
flair / flare
flea / flee
forth / fourth
frays / phrase
frees / frieze
gait / gate
gamble / gambol
gilt / guilt
graft / graphed
grate / great
groan / grown
guessed / guest
guise / guys
hail / hale
hair / hare
hall / haul
hangar / hanger
heal / heel
heard / herd
hew / hue
higher / hire
hoard / horde
hoarse / horse
hoes / hose

hole / whole
humerus / humorous
incidence / incidents
incite / insight
intense / intents
jam / jamb
jibe / gibe
key / quay
knead / need
knows / nose
lacks / lax
laps / lapse
lea / lee
leach / leech
lead / led
leak / leek
leased / least
leaver / lever
lessen / lesson
links / lynx
loan / lone
made / maid
mail / male
maize / maze
manners / manors
mantel / mantle
marshal / martial
medal / meddle
metal / mettle
might / mite
miners / minors

Homophones Word List

miscible / missable
moan / mown
moose / mousse
morn / mourn
muscle / mussel
mustard / mustered
naval / navel
none / nun
oar / ore
ode / owed
one / won
overseas / oversees
paced / paste
packed / pact
pail / pale
pain / pane
palate / pallet
passed / past
patience / patients
peace / piece
peal / peel
pear / pare
pedal / peddle
peeked / piqued
peer / pier
perse / purse
place / plaice
pleas / please
plum / plumb

pole / poll
pore / pour
presence / presents
preys / praise
pride / pried
pries / prize
profit / prophet
racket / racquet
rain / reign
rays / raze
recede / reseed
receipt / reseat
reek / wreak
relaid / relayed
retch / wretch
road / rowed
roll / role
root / route
rough / ruff
rows / rose
rued / rude
rues / ruse
rye / wry
sail / sale
saver / savour
scene / seen
scull / skull
seas / seize
serf / surf

serge / surge
sheer / shear
side / sighed
sighs / size
sight / cite
sites / sights
slay / sleigh
sleight / slight
soar / sore
soared / sword
sole / soul
some / sum
stake / steak
stationary / stationery
stayed / staid
steal / steel
stile / style
storey / story
straight / strait
sty / stye
succour / sucker
suede / swayed
suite / sweet
summary / summery
taught / taut
tear / tier
teeming / teaming
tense / tents
threw / through

throws / throes
time / thyme
tire / tyre
toad / towed
told / tolled
tracked / tract
trussed / trust
unreal / unreel
use / ewes
vain / vane
vale / veil
vial / vile
wail / whale
waist / waste
wait / weight
waive / wave
war / wore
wares / wears
wax / whacks
weakly / weekly
wet / whet
whined / wind
whirl / whorl
whirred / word
wield / wheeled
wine / whine
wood / would
worst / wurst
yoke / yolk

Congratulations!

You have now learnt **700** homonyms;
know what they mean and how to use
them in a sentence.

We hope that you have enjoyed
completing the series of books and that
we have helped you increase your word
power skills.

PROGRESS CHARTS

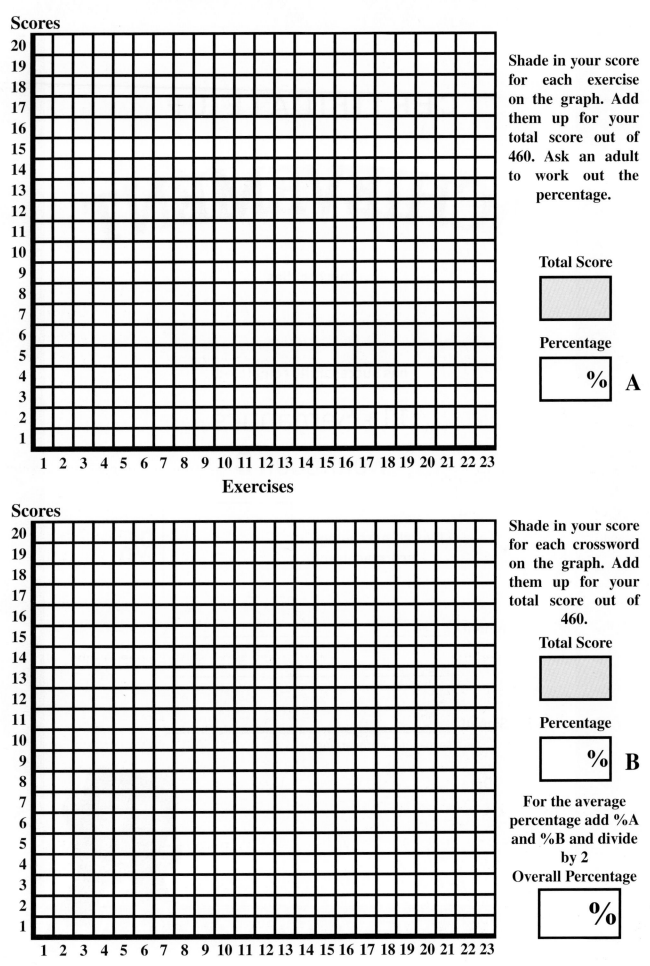

Shade in your score for each exercise on the graph. Add them up for your total score out of 460. Ask an adult to work out the percentage.

Total Score

Percentage

% **A**

Shade in your score for each crossword on the graph. Add them up for your total score out of 460.

Total Score

Percentage

% **B**

For the average percentage add %A and %B and divide by 2

Overall Percentage

%

CERTIFICATE OF

ACHIEVEMENT

This certifies

_____

has successfully completed

11+ Semantics

WORKBOOK **3**

Overall percentage
score achieved

[ ] **%**

Comment _____

_____

Signed _____

(teacher/parent/guardian)

Date _____